How to Draw
the Craziest, Creepiest
Characters

www.raintreepublishers.co.uk
Visit our website to find out
more information about
Raintree books.

To order:
☎ Phone 0845 6044371
🖹 Fax +44 (0) 1865 312263
✉ Email myorders@raintreepublishers.co.uk

Customers from outside the UK please telephone +44 1865 312262

Raintree is an imprint of Capstone Global Library Limited, a company incorporated in
England and Wales having its registered office at 7 Pilgrim Street, London EC4V 6LB
Registered company number: 6695882

Text © Capstone Press 2012
First published by Capstone Press in 2012
First published in paperback in the United Kingdom by Capstone Global Library in 2012
The moral rights of the proprietor have been asserted.

ISBN 978 1 406 24294 2 (paperback)
16 15 14 13 12
10 9 8 7 6 5 4 3 2 1

British Library Cataloguing in Publication Data
Singh, Asavari.
How to draw the craziest, creepiest characters.
741.5'1-dc23
A full catalogue record for this book is available from the British Library.

Author: Asavari Singh
Editor: Laura Knowles
Art Director: Joita Das
Designer: Deepika Verma, Isha Khanna, Navneet Kaur
Colouring Artists: Aadil Ahmed Siddiqui, Abhijeet Sharma, Danish Zaidi,
Priyanka Singh, Madhavi Poddar, Vinay Kumar Sharma
Line Artists: Deepak Kumar, Ishan Varma, Martin James, Nishant Mudgal,
Prithwiraj Samat, Surendra Kumar Tripathi
Originated by Capstone Global Library
Printed and bound in China by Leo Paper Products Ltd

CONTENTS

CHAPTER 1
CREATING CHARACTERS   **4**

CHAPTER 2
FACE OFF   **8**

CHAPTER 3
BODY BUILDING   **12**

CHAPTER 4
STYLE STATEMENTS   **18**

CHAPTER 5
CRAZY CHARACTERS   **22**

CHAPTER 6
THE UNDEAD   **26**

CHAPTER 7
GIRL POWER   **30**

CHAPTER 8
MONSTERS   **36**

CHAPTER 9
PEN, PAPER, ACTION!   **42**

FIND OUT MORE   **48**

CREATING CHARACTERS

A comic or graphic novel without cool characters is like a superhero without big muscles — it's just not right! Use this book and your imagination to create characters that pop right off the page.

Before You begin

Great characters don't come out of thin air. You have to create them before you transfer them onto paper!

- ✓ **Look for inspiration:** It's everywhere! It could be an existing comic book character, a TV or movie star, or someone you know.

- ✓ **Personality:** What kind of person is your character? Good, evil, or a bit of both? Is he or she funny, angry, silly, smart, sneaky, or a combination of some of these traits?

- ✓ **The back story:** Ask yourself questions about your character. Start with age, family background, friends, and career. What does he or she care about? What conflicts does he or she have to face?

- ✓ **Looks:** Body type can say a lot about your character. Is he or she large and muscular? Tall and thin? Short and round?

What are archetypes?

Heroes, villains, warriors, monsters, and so on are all archetypes. This means they each have a set of defining characteristics. You should be able to guess their role in a story just by looking at them.

Witch: Her job is to create mischief and magic wherever she goes.

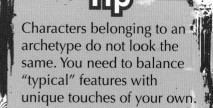

Tip

Characters belonging to an archetype do not look the same. You need to balance "typical" features with unique touches of your own.

Monster: They are not like people or most animals, so you never know what they'll do next. Life and property are in danger around them.

Heroes and heroines are generally fit and muscular. Monsters and villains often look mean. Goofy characters work well with exaggerated cartoon-like features.

Brainiac: He's always plotting and scheming. You decide whether it's for good or evil!

Chapter 2

FACE OFF

The face is probably the most important part of a character. Here's how to get it right, step by step.

Basic faces

Draw a circle for the top half of the face. Use straight lines to make the jaw.

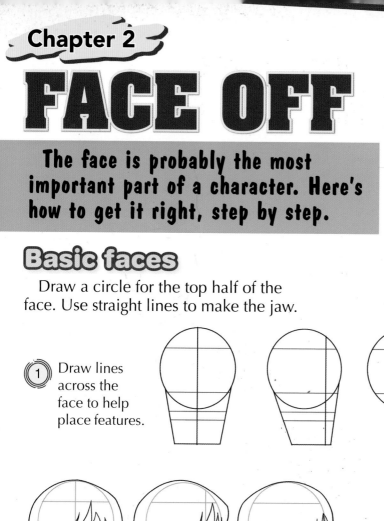

(1) Draw lines across the face to help place features.

(2) Place features and define the jaw.

(3) Add details to the features and hair.

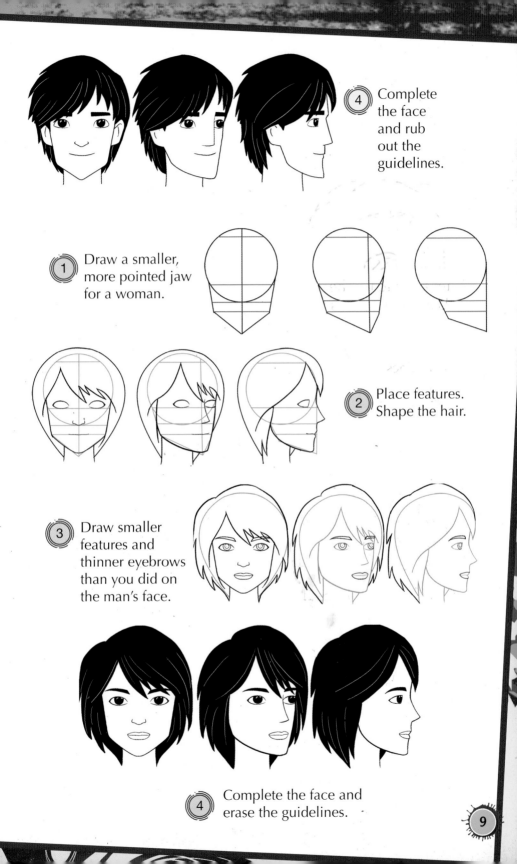

4 Complete the face and rub out the guidelines.

1 Draw a smaller, more pointed jaw for a woman.

2 Place features. Shape the hair.

3 Draw smaller features and thinner eyebrows than you did on the man's face.

4 Complete the face and erase the guidelines.

Expressions

Facial expressions speak louder than words. They provide instant information about how a character is feeling.

SNEAKY

One raised eyebrow, half smile

HAPPY

Lips upturned, eyebrows slightly raised

ANGRY

Eyebrows drawn together, teeth showing

STERN

Slightly narrowed eyes, lips pursed

SCARED

Eyebrows raised, eyes wide, mouth open

SURPRISED

Lips in an "O", eyebrows raised

CONFUSED

Eyes wide, one eyebrow raised

SAD

Mouth turned down, eyes narrow

DISGUSTED

Nose wrinkled, frowning

Chapter 3

Body Building

Learn to draw basic male and female figures before you try out different body types and postures.

Bones and flesh

Start your drawing with a simple stick figure. Make small circles where the joints should be. Draw rough outlines for the hands and feet.

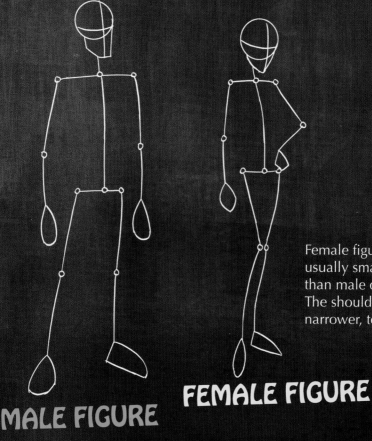

Female figures are usually smaller than male ones. The shoulders are narrower, too.

MALE FIGURE

FEMALE FIGURE

Add some flesh! Use solid shapes to get a three-dimensional look. For example, you can make tubes for the limbs, balls for the joints, and curved rectangles for the chest.

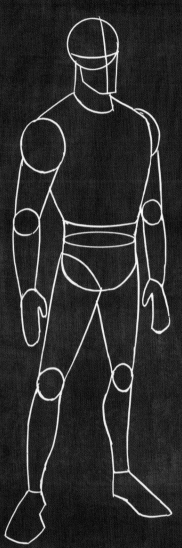

Female figures have rounder hips and narrower waists. Their arms and legs are more curvy, too.

Tip

Use the joints to guide proportions. The arms and legs will taper off from these points on the body.

Dynamic posing

Get your stick figure moving! Experiment with a variety of different poses. Walking, kicking, swooping, leaping, and fighting are just some of the actions you can show.

Flesh out the stick figures. Body parts look different in different poses, so it's a bit tricky. Practice until you get the proportions right.

Caricatures

Cartoons and caricatures give you the freedom to blow body parts and features out of proportion or squeeze them skinny. It all depends on the kind of character you're drawing.

The massive muscles, heavy jaw, and mean eyes on this boxer spell danger.

Tip

For practice, draw a normal body and then make a caricature version of it. If the muscles are big, make them humongous. If the frame is skinny, make it like a skeleton. If the eyes are big, go for a glare.

This lightweight won't scare anyone. His drooping eyes, silly smile, slouching spine, and spindly limbs make him look like a sloppy slacker.

This character doesn't look strong, but he has tons of energy! It's all in the eyes, smile, and posture.

Chapter 4

STYLE STATEMENTS

A good drawing of a character becomes great once you add colour, a costume, and other cool touches.

Clothes and accessories

You can tell a lot about characters from the clothes they wear. Clothes can give information about everything from a profession to how rich a character is.

Superheroes prefer tight-fitting outfits that help define their powerful muscles. Underwear worn over clothes is optional!

Traditional witches usually wear loose clothes, ride a broom, and wear a pointy hat. Make sure to show wrinkles on the clothes.

Tip

A prop is sometimes called character scenery. It adds lots of information about your character. For example, glasses indicate that a character is brainy, while eye patches hint at criminal activities.

Pirates usually wear a vest and loose trousers called pantaloons. They often have broken teeth or a missing eye, which is covered by an eye patch.

Shades and colours

The way you use colour or even black or white is important. It sets the mood for the entire picture.

Draw in black and white to create a dark look with lots of atmosphere.

Tip

Change the colour of a character's face to show extreme emotions. Red works for anger, green for sick, and white for scared.

The colours that characters wear give hints about their personality. This bright outfit makes the vampire look relatively harmless.

The deeper colours here make the vampire look more serious and scary.

Chapter 5

CRAZY CHARACTERS

The world is full of all kinds of characters! Be creative!

The Goofy Genius

He's a genius who likes pushing buttons. Naturally, he's always getting into trouble.

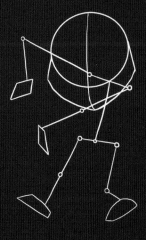

1 Start with a stick figure in a dynamic pose. Make the head a little too big for the body.

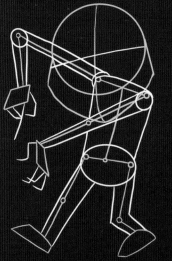

2 Flesh out the stick figure. Since he'll be shown using a remote control, make sure you draw one finger pointing down.

3 Shape the features, clothes, and hair. You could draw his eyebrows above his head to give him a comical expression.

4 Complete the clothes and remote control. Add glasses. The grin gives a full view of his teeth and tongue.

5 Fill in a background. Something that looks like a science lab should work.

23

Tiny Transformer

Who wouldn't like a little robot rolling around the house like a unicycle? But watch out – he can be quite a handful!

(1) Since the transformer isn't human, stick to basic geometric shapes for the outline. Don't forget to give it arms and fingers.

(2) Fill out the shapes to make the robot look three-dimensional. Turn the circle at the base into a wheel.

(3) Transformers have faces, too. Draw one on for yours, and don't forget to give it a mouth.

4 Add details to the body in the form of buttons and screens. Finish the arms.

Fact

Famous robot characters include Megatron from the *Transformer* series, Awesome Android in *Fantastic Four*, and Superman's enemy Brainiac.

5 Draw a background. Make it look modern and high-tech. Use different shades of grey to show metal.

Chapter 6

THE UNDEAD

If you crave chills and thrills, you need a good dose of undead. And what safer way to spend time with them than to draw them?

Zombie

Fresh from the grave and ready to munch on some human brains, all zombies have one thing in common – they're gross!

1. Draw a stick figure. The limbs should be twisted – it's a result of coffin cramp.

2. The body should be all skin and bones. Make the face long so the jaw can hang open.

3. Outline the face and some tattered clothes. Give the zombie blank, staring eyes.

4 Add tufts of hair, rotting teeth, and long nails.

Fact

The word "zombie" comes from a Haitian word that means spirit of the dead. *White Zombie*, which came out in 1932, was the first film featuring these undead creatures.

5 To make the zombie feel at home, draw a cemetery around him. A full moon adds to the drama. Use dark colours.

R.I

R.I.P

The Bloodsucker

Vampires dress as sharply as they bite. If they bring you home for dinner, you're probably the main dish.

1 Draw a stick figure. The joints should be tiny since the body is very lean.

2 Flesh out the figure, making sure the shoulders are wider than the hips.

3 Dress up your vampire in trousers, a vest, and a long overcoat. Draw his eyes, mouth, and hair.

4. Add details to the clothes and hands. Make sure his hair, scarf, and cape are moving in the same direction. Don't forget his fangs.

Fact

Count Dracula was easily the most famous bloodsucker until the world met Edward Cullen and his family in the *Twilight* series.

5. To give your bloodsucker a spooky background, add the outline of a castle, a full moon, and bats. Shade the castle and bats black.

Chapter 7

GIRL POWER

They're battling bad guys one day and hanging out with friends the next. Either way, there's just no stopping these girls.

Woman on Wheels

This girl knows where she's headed and she's taking the fastest route to get there. You can try asking her for a lift, but be prepared to see her zoom past.

1 Start with a stick figure. Her body should lean back. Draw a curved line to help mark her position on the bike.

2 Add flesh to the body and draw fists. Make a pair of wheels.

3 Let her hair flow behind her and outline the clothes and bike.

Tip

You can transform the Woman on Wheels into a traditional warrior princess by substituting the bike for a horse and changing the clothing.

4 No biker is complete without a cool pair of boots and goggles.

5 Add details to the bike.
Draw headlights and wing
mirrors. Make the outline
of the wheels.

6 Shade the area near
the wheels. Draw lines
behind the bike to show
movement.

7 Draw the background, such as a road and pavement.

8 Give the bike a bright colour, and add funky graphics.

Teenage Witch

There's magic in the air when she's around.
She uses a mobile phone instead of a wand
but will not leave home without her pointy hat.

1 Start with a stick figure.
Your witch can fly,
so draw her hovering
above the ground.

2 Flesh out the stick
figure to make
it look three-
dimensional. The
legs should be
slightly crossed.

3 Outline some trendy
clothes for your teen
witch. And don't forget
her hat. Shape her hair so
that it shows movement.

Add details to her clothes and shoes. Draw her magical phone, and give her a fun expression.

 Witches no longer wear just black! Use bright colours for the clothes. Give her hair a colour that's not natural to add to the magical effect.

Chapter 8

MONSTERS

The best thing about monsters is that they can be as scary as you like. They are all about big bodies and big movements.

The Half Beast

He has the head of a wolf and the body of a pro wrestler. Do not approach.

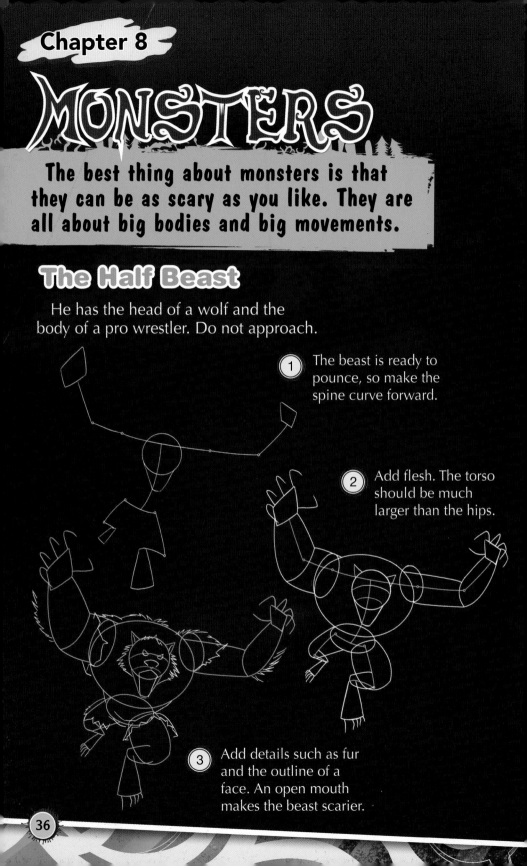

1 The beast is ready to pounce, so make the spine curve forward.

2 Add flesh. The torso should be much larger than the hips.

3 Add details such as fur and the outline of a face. An open mouth makes the beast scarier.

Define muscles and claws. Give him an angry expression and very sharp teeth.

5 Add details to the scene, such as the hole in the fence that the Half Beast just made.

The Marsh Monster

This monster hides in the darkest, slimiest depths of a swamp. When he does come out, the ground trembles – as do his victims.

1 Draw a stick figure in an action position. Leave lots of room for muscles.

2 Draw a box over the body. This will help define his hunched-over, bulky shape.

Shape the shoulders and arms over the box. Add a face and define the claws.

 Outline his face. His mouth is open in a roar. Erase the guidelines and draw in his chest muscles.

5 Define the joints and muscles. Draw some teeth and webbed spines on his back.

6 Add scales to the body. Draw slimy water dripping from his fingers.

7. Draw the marsh. The water near his feet should be rippled to show movement.

8. A dull yellowish-green gives the monster a slime-coated look. Use off-white with ribbons of black to make the water look as filthy as possible.

Chapter 9

PEN, PAPER, ACTION!

A character's job is to tell a story. But they can't usually do this alone. A good story puts two or more characters in interesting situations — usually a conflict of some sort.

King of the lab

This is the ultimate fight for power over science. Who will come out on top? Our goofy scientist or his invention, the unicycling robot?

Tip

Pay attention to the background. The setting will help pull your story together.

Monster mayhem

This match between the Half Beast and the Marsh Monster is bound to get loud. It's not for those who are easily scared!

The wrong victim

The Bloodsucker is hungry and this girl looks like the perfect victim – but only to him. She's all ready to battle!

WHAT NEXT?

Now that you can draw a range of different character types, use your imagination! Think of other exciting characters you could create. Whether it's aliens, talking animals, fairies, or new and improved versions of famous characters, the possibilities are endless. Get started!

Find out more

To learn how to draw other fantastic characters, or create a manga comic strip, why not look at some of these books.

The Art of Drawing Manga, Ben Krefta (Arcturus Books, 2009)

Drawing Cartoons (Usbourne Art Ideas), Anna Milbourne (Usbourne, 2010)

How to Draw Comic Heroes, Aaron Sautter (Edge Books, 2007)

How to Draw Disgusting Aliens, Aaron Sautter (Edge Books, 2007)

How to Draw Ferocious Animals, Aaron Sautter (Edge Books, 2008)

How to Draw Magical Creatures and Mythical Beasts, Mark Bergin (Book House, 2007)

How to Draw Manga Warriors, Aaron Sautter (Edge Books, 2007)